Gold Stars

This book belongs to:

....

 I read the first story!

 I read the second story!

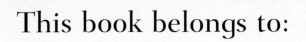 I read the third story!

Level 3

Stories to Read

Written by Sue Graves
Illustrated by Paula Martyr, and Jan Smith

Language consultant: Betty Root

This is a Parragon book
This edition published in 2003

Parragon
Queen Street House
4 Queen Street
Bath, BA1 1HE, UK

ISBN 1-40542-814-7
Printed in China

Gold Stars

Stories to Read

Three Level 3 Stories

p

Contents

Notes for Parents

Reading with your child is an enjoyable and rewarding experience. **Gold Stars Stories to Read** encourage and support children who are learning to read.

There are four different reading levels within the **Stories to Read** series. Within each level, the books can be read in any order. The steps between the levels are deliberately small because it is so important, at this early stage, for children to succeed. Success creates confidence.

Starting to read

Start by reading the story aloud to your child, taking time to talk about the pictures. This will help your child to see that pictures often give clues about the story.

Over a period of time, try to read the same story several times so that your child becomes familiar with the story and the words and phrases. Then your child will be ready to read the story aloud with you. It helps to run your finger under the words as you say them.

Occasionally, stop and encourage your child to continue reading aloud without you. Join in again when your child needs help. This is the next step towards helping your child become an independent reader.

Finally, your child will be ready to read alone. Listen carefully to your child and give plenty of praise and encouragement.

Using your Gold Stars stickers

You can use the **Gold Stars** stickers as a reward for effort as well as achievement. Learning to read is an exciting challenge for every child.

Remember these four important stages:

- Read the story **to** your child.
- Read the story **with** your child.
- Encourage your child to read **to you**.
- Listen to your child read **alone**.

Tiger's Spots

Tiger had lots of stripes. He had lots of stripes all over him.

Tiger was very proud of his stripes.
"I'm so stripy," he said.

Every day, Tiger went to look
in the pool. He liked to look
in the pool to see his stripes.

Wow!

He looked this way. He looked
that way. "Wow! I'm so stripy,"
he said.

But one day, Tiger had a big surprise. He looked in the pool, and he looked again. Tiger could see lots and lots of spots!

"Help!" said Tiger. "I'm so spotty!
And I'm so itchy!"

Tiger was sad. He sniffed a loud sniff. His tears fell into the pool. Plop, plop!

"I must get rid of my spots,"
said Tiger. "I'll ask Monkey.
She will help me."

Tiger went to find Monkey. She was swinging from a branch high up in the trees.

"Monkey, look at my spots!" said Tiger. "I'm so spotty and itchy. Can you help me?"

Monkey looked at Tiger. She laughed and swung to the next branch.

"A spotty tiger! I've never seen a spotty tiger before," said Monkey. "Ask Snake. He will help you."

Tiger went to find Snake. He was snoozing in the long grass.

"Snake, look at my spots!" said Tiger. "I'm so spotty and itchy. Can you help me?"

Snake looked at Tiger. He hissed
and shook his head.

"A spotty tiger! I've never seen a
spotty tiger before," said Snake.
"Ask Elephant. She will help you."

Tiger went to find Elephant. She was busy washing.

"Elephant, look at my spots!" said Tiger. "I'm so spotty and itchy. Can you help me?"

Elephant looked at Tiger. She lifted her trunk and trumpeted loudly.

"A spotty tiger! I've never seen a spotty tiger before," said Elephant. "Ask Orang-utan. She will help you."

Tiger went to find Orang-utan.

"Orang-utan, look at my spots!" said Tiger. "I'm so spotty and itchy. Can you help me?"

Orang-utan looked at Tiger's spots.
Then she scratched her head.

"You have chicken pox,"
said Orang-utan.

You have chicken pox.

"That's why you are so spotty and
itchy. But don't worry, you'll soon
feel better."

Orang-utan made a bed of soft leaves for Tiger. She gave him a long, cool drink. She splashed cool water onto him.

"Try to stop scratching those itchy spots," said Orang-utan.

Tiger lay on the bed of soft leaves.
"I feel a little better," he said.

A few days later, Orang-utan took Tiger to the pool.

"Look in the pool, Tiger," she said. "What do you see?"

Tiger looked in the pool. He looked this way. He looked that way.

"Wow! I'm so stripy," he said. "Thank you, Orang-utan!"

Read each sentence. The pictures will help you.

had lots of stripes.

Tiger went to find

looked at Tiger.

lifted her trunk.

looked at Tiger's spots.

Orang-utan made a bed
of soft   .

Big Digger
Helps Out

Big Digger is very big. Big Digger has a big bucket. The bucket can dig holes and move bricks.

Bert drives Big Digger. Bert and Big
Digger work together.

Sometimes Bert and Big Digger work in the town. They help to dig holes in the road. They help fill in holes too.

Bert and Big Digger like digging
holes. But it can be very noisy!

Sometimes Bert and Big Digger work on the building site. Big Digger has to move bricks on the building site.

Bert and Big Digger like working
on the building site. But it can be
very noisy!

One day, Bert and Big Digger got a phone call. The phone call was from Mr Smith.

"Hello, Bert," said Mr Smith.
"I have lots of old bricks to move
from the building site. Can you and
Big Digger help?"

Bert and Big Digger went to the building site. They met Mr Smith.

"I want you to put the old bricks over there," said Mr Smith.

"Leave it to us, Mr Smith,"
said Bert.

Bert and Big Digger set to work.

Just then, Bert saw Little Bird. Little Bird was sitting on her eggs. The eggs were in a nest. The nest was on top of an old drainpipe.

"Oh, no!" said Bert. "Look at that nest, Big Digger. That is not a safe place for eggs."

Oh, no!

49

Bert put lots of straw into Big
Digger's bucket.
Big Digger lifted up his bucket.

He lifted it up to the top of the old drainpipe. Big Digger lifted the nest and the eggs into his bucket.

Big Digger moved the eggs to a tree.

"We will make a safe nest in the tree," said Bert. Bert and Little Bird made a safe new nest.

Big Digger lifted up his bucket.
He lifted it up to the new nest.
Bert put the eggs in the new nest.

Tweet, tweet!

"Look at Little Bird, Big Digger!"
said Bert. "Look at Little Bird in her
new nest. Now the eggs will be safe."

Little Bird sat on her eggs in her new nest.

"Now we must wait for the eggs to hatch," said Bert.

A few days later, Bert and Big Digger heard a noise. The noise was coming from the nest in the tree.

Tweet, tweet!

"Look, Big Digger!" said Bert. "The eggs have hatched. Thank you for helping Little Bird, Big Digger.

Read each sentence. The pictures will help you.

Bert and  work together.

Bert saw Little .

Little Bird was sitting on her .

Big Digger took the
to the tree.

Bert made a nest in the   .

put the eggs in the nest.

Silly Pig Has an Idea

This is Silly Pig. Everyone calls her Silly Pig because she does silly things!

"You silly pig!" said Horse. "Pigs don't put flowers on their heads!"

One day, Silly Pig had an idea. She went to tell the other animals about her idea.

"I'm going to look for treasure on the farm," she said. "I'm going to find lots and lots of treasure."

"You silly pig!" said the other animals. "You won't find treasure on the farm."

Silly Pig set off to look for treasure. She went out of the farmyard and up the lane.

Suddenly, Silly Pig stopped. She saw something sparkling in the tree.

"Ooh! I can see a sparkling necklace in the tree. A sparkling necklace is treasure. I shall put it around my neck."

But the sparkling necklace wasn't really a necklace. It was a spider's web. The web was sparkling with raindrops.

Spider was very cross. "What a silly
thing to do," he said. "You silly pig!"

Silly Pig felt very silly. She set off up the lane.

Suddenly, Silly Pig stopped. She saw something sparkling in the hedge.

"Ooh! I can see sparkling earrings in the hedge," she said. "Sparkling earrings are treasure. I shall put them on my ears."

But the sparkling earrings weren't really earrings. They were red berries by a bird's nest. The berries were sparkling in the sun.

Blackbird was very cross. "What a silly thing to do!" he said. "You silly pig!"

Silly Pig felt very silly. She set off up the lane.

Suddenly, Silly Pig stopped. She saw something sparkling in the mud.

"Ooh! I can see something sparkling in the mud," she said. "It must be treasure!"

Silly Pig pulled the sparkling thing out of the mud.

"Oh dear!" said Silly Pig. "It's only a ring. What silly treasure! I can't put a ring around my neck or on my ears."

Silly Pig picked up the ring. She took
it back to the farm.

Farmer Kate was in the farmyard. She saw Silly Pig. Then she saw the ring.

"Hello, Silly Pig!" she said. "What have you got there?" She took the ring from Silly Pig.

What have you got there?

"My ring!" said Farmer Kate. "You have found my ring, Silly Pig!"

Farmer Kate gave Silly Pig a big hug.
"Thank you for finding my ring," she
said. "You clever pig!"

You clever pig!

Read each sentence. The pictures
will help you.

Silly Pig saw something
sparkling in the

The  was sparkling with
raindrops.

The  was very cross.

Silly  felt very silly.

Silly Pig picked up the  .

She took it back to the 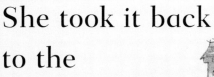 .

Gold Stars

Level 3 stories are for
beginner readers who can read
short sentences with help.

- More detailed stories
- Builds essential vocabulary
- Speech bubbles repeat words
  from the main text
- Lively pictures to support
  the text
- Sentence review activity

Gold Stars

Gold Stars Stories to Read
encourage and support
children who are learning to read.

Level 1: for children who are ready
to begin learning to read.

Level 2: for children who can recognize
simple words and phrases.

Level 3: for beginner readers who can
read short sentences with help.

Level 4: for more confident readers
who are beginning to read
alone.